How To Handle Your Cat

Scholastic Children's Books,
Commonwealth House, 1-19 New Oxford Street,
London WC1A 1NU, UK
a division of Scholastic Ltd
London ~ New York ~ Toronto ~ Sydney ~ Auckland
Mexico City ~ New Delhi ~ Hong Kong

First published in the UK by Scholastic Ltd, 2001

ISBN 0 439 99222 2

All rights reserved
Typeset by TW Typesetting, Midsomer Norton, Somerset
Printed by Cox & Wyman Ltd, Reading, Berks

10 9 8 7 6 5 4 3 2 1

How To Handle Your Cat

By Roy Apps

Illustrated by Jo Moore

Hippo

Contents

It was another dark and stormy night...
The wind howled in the trees. The trees
howled in the wind. Thunder roared.
Lightning struck. And it started to rain cats
and dogs.

The noise got worse. This was because not
only was the wind howling, the cats and
dogs were, too. Not only that, there was a
ringing coming from the kitchen.

I went into the house and made for the
kitchen. The ringing was coming from a little
black box on the worktop. I picked it up.*

"Yes, what is it?" I enquired.

"It's your mobile phone, of course, you
dumbo," said my phone. "What do you think
it is, a bowl of muesli?"

Most people have an Answerphone. I,
however, have got an Answerbackphone.**

*The little black box that is, not the worktop.
**Those of you who have read *How To Handle Your Dog* will, of course,
know this.

"Easy mistake to make," I told my Answerbackphone. "You are rather like a bowl of muesli, being, as it were, a little nutty."

My soaking sleeves were dripping all over it.

"Urgh! I'm wringing wet!" grumbled my phone.

"Not so much wringing wet, more like *ringing* wet!" I chortled.

"Cut the lip and listen," retorted my Answerbackphone. "About the other night—"

"The other dark and stormy night?"

"Yes, that other night... There were a couple of messages left on me for you and you only heard one of them.* I think you should hear the second one."

"I don't pay you to think," I said. "I pay you to take my messages."

*Those of you who have read *How To Handle Your Dog* will know this, too. And even those of you who *haven't* read *How To Handle Your Dog* will know this now, 'cos you've just read it.

There was a blip and a bleep and a blurp. Then my Answerbackphone played me back the second message:

> *Hello...? Could you come and see me? It's my Tiddles. Thank you. Oh, by the way, it's Kit Katt here.*

I was out of the door in one second. And I was flat on my drive in another second. Mainly because I tripped up over all the cats and dogs that had been raining down.

I picked myself up. This was quite difficult, because I am very heavy. Then I got into my van and drove to Kit Katt's house.

Now, if you've already read the other half of the book, you may well be wondering what I, Luke Dogwalker, am doing going to visit someone who has a problem with a *cat*.

Well, as I said on page 10 of *How To Handle Your Dog*, I am not one but *two* very special people. When I'm in my Rover, I'm Luke Dogwalker. When I'm in my Purrsche, I'm Meow-gli.

Who on earth is Meow-Gli?

I told you – *I* am!

Bit of a stupid name, isn't it?

Listen sunshine, compared to most of the names in this book, it's a very *sensible* name. You've heard of *The Jungle Book*, those stories about a hero called Mowgli who understood the ways of the wild beasts?

Yes

Well, I'm *Meow-gli*, a hero who understands the ways of even wilder beasts.

Mowgli   Meow-gli

I screeched to a halt outside Kit Katt's house...

TO A HALT!!!

The door was opened by a guy wearing outsized shoes, who had a worried expression on his face and who was standing on his head. There was no doubt about it, he was a clown with a frown standing upside down.

"Hi!" said this clown, holding out his hand. "I'm Kit Katt. Known as 'Cool' Katt."

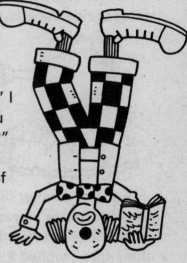

"Could've fooled me," I muttered. "Why are you standing on your head?"

" 'Cos I've just been reading the other half of this book," the clown replied. "Do you know, it's been printed the wrong way up!"

I started to explain that it would be easier to turn the book, rather than yourself, upside down, but I gave up. I was getting a crick in my neck trying to talk to him.

Eventually he stood up the right way.

"Another thing," I said. "Why are you dressed like a clown?"

"Am I?" asked Kit.

"Yes! Those enormous shoes," I replied.

"They must be about ten sizes too big for you."

"Eleven sizes too big, actually," said Kit. "My mum bought them that size deliberately. She said I'd grow into them. That's why she's filled them up with manure and told me to water them every day."

"And yet another thing," I continued. "Why are you looking so worried?"

"You'd be worried if your shoes were full of manure," replied Kit. "But there is something else." Kit paused. "It's Tiddles."

"Ah yes," I said. "You mentioned Tiddles in your phone message."

"You mean *you're* the Pets Resc-You person?" enquired Kit, in a surprised voice.

"I am. Why do you look so amazed?"

Kit thought long and hard. "You don't look like a pet expert."

"What do you expect a pet expert to look like?" I asked.

"A normal human being?" suggested Kit, watering his feet.

"Why should I look like Ann Ormalhumanbeing," I said. "We're not related or anything. Now, what's the problem with Tiddles?"

Meow-gli   Ann Ormalhummanbeing

"He's trying to learn to fly," said Kit.

"A common enough problem with cats," I replied. "And one I can help you with. First of all, it will be helpful for you to learn where cats come from."

"Why don't you come into the house?" asked Kit.

"For a start, I can't get over your shoes," I said.

"And I can't get over your fake leopard skin leotard," said Kit.

How To Handle Your Cat: Stage one

Learning Where Cats Come From

Ten minutes later, I sat down in Kit's sitting room and explained about the ancestry of cats.

"You see," I began. "Thousands of years ago, when mammoths roamed the land, men hunted with clubs and your gran had just started knitting that orange and mauve teletubbies jumper she's promised you for your birthday, there were gruesome creatures called sabre-toothed tigers."

Kit nodded.

"These sabre-toothed tigers aren't to be confused with cyber-toothed tigers, which are virtual pets or tomagotchis."

ROAR!

bleep

Kit nodded again.

"Your twenty-first-century pet cat is descended from these sabre-toothed tigers."

"I know that," said Kit.

"*I* know that," I said. "But your cat doesn't know that."

"Perhaps I should tell him then," suggested Kit.

"It wouldn't do any good," I said. "He wouldn't take any notice of you. Cats don't believe all that stuff about sabre-toothed tigers, men hunting with clubs and grans knitting orange and mauve jumpers."

"What do they believe they're descended from, then?" asked Kit.

"Well, as they like to think of themselves as a superior kind of beast, cats believe themselves to have evolved from a whole variety of creatures into a kind of super-animal. Your Tiddles obviously thinks he's descended from a bird. In fact, he's a prime example of a category of top cat that us at Pets Resc-You call a Bird Cat."

How To Handle Your Cat: Stage two

Learning About the Top Catty-gories
Top Catty-gory No. 1: **The Bird Cat**

At that moment, something launched itself off the top shelf of the bookcase. It circled the chandelier with its legs outstretched like wings, before landing on the top of my head.

"Mee-ow!" said Tiddles.

"Me! Owwwww!" I replied.

"Tiddles!" cried Kit. "Here pussy-wussy!" But Tiddles had gone. Pausing only to dig his claws in my ears, he had re- launched himself through the window ...

... and out into the garden ...

... where he climbed ...

... a tree

... which he proceeded to ...

... throw ...

... himself off of ...

... narrowly missing ...

... Kit's dad's lawn-mower.

"You see why I'm so worried," said Kit. "He could really hurt himself doing that."

"It's not *him* getting hurt I'm worried about," I replied, rubbing the top of my head, where Tiddles had dug his claws in.

"So, how do I handle him?" asked Kit.

"The first thing you've got to stop him doing is landing on your head," I advised. "There are two ways of doing this, which I explain in full details on this Fcat Sheet—"

"What's a Fcat Sheet?" asked Kit.

"It's a Fact Sheet with f-acts about f-cats, of course," I replied. And it looks like this..."

FCAT SHEET 1: TWO WAYS TO STOP A CAT LANDING ON YOUR HEAD

1. Nod your head all the time. That way it will never be still enough for Tiddles to land on and he'll find somewhere else to land – with any luck, your big sister's head.

SLIGHT PROBLEM WITH THIS METHOD: Nod your head too much and it's likely to fall off. Once it's on the floor, it'll stop nodding and your cat can land on it to his heart's content.

---

2. Put something on top of your head that's going to make your cat so scared when he sees it, he'll change course in mid-flight and land somewhere else. The sort of thing your Bird Cat is likely to be scared of is a Large Dog. If you don't have a picture of a Large Dog, use the one on page 20.

SLIGHT PROBLEM WITH THIS METHOD: Your dog might see the picture on your head and decide to pick a fight with it.

"Now, I must go," I explained. "I have a text message on my mobile."

HELP! MY CAT HAS
A DEATH WISH —
EVE NINGALL

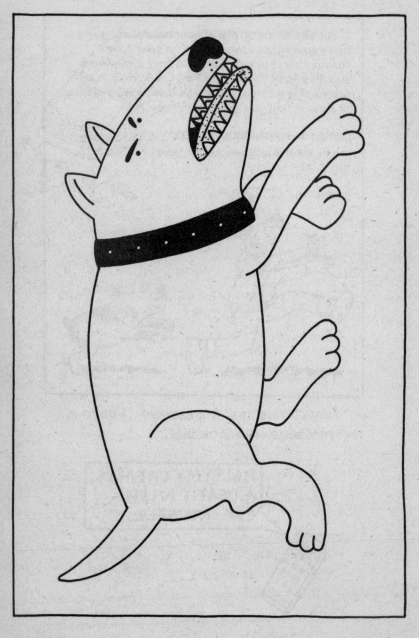

As you've probably guessed, Eve Ningall's dad was a police officer.

My Purr-sche was racing up Eve's road when I had to hit the brakes hard. (The brakes were so cross they hit me back.) Then Eve came running out of her house.

"Oh, Miffkins, are you all right?"

"My name isn't Miffkins," I said, crossly. "Although I am kind of miffed."

"I wasn't talking to you," said Eve. "I was talking to my cat. You almost ran her over!"

"She dashed out in front of my Purr-sche," I said.

"I know," said Eve. "She's always doing it. It's a real problem. That's why I sent for you."

"I'm sure I can help you handle her," I replied. "I *am* an expert."

Eve frowned. "You don't look like an expert," she said.

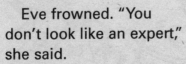

"Let's get on, shall we?" I snapped.

"You sound in a huff," said Eve.

"I'm not in a huff!" I replied.

"I can see," answered Eve. "You're in a fake leopard-skin leotard."

"I'll ignore your attitude," I said.

"I wish I could ignore your fake leopard-skin leotard," muttered Eve.

I pulled myself up to my full height. Unfortunately, that meant my head went right through the roof of the Purr-sche, so I had to pull myself down again.

"So," I continued, "your little Miffkins keeps running out in the road in front of cars?"

"Worse than that," said Eve, "he runs out in front of my brother's skateboard."

"The reason Miffkins keeps running across the road playing chicken is he thinks he *is* a chicken. He's what we at Pets Resc-You call a Chicken Cat. Which is the official veterinary name for a cat who's always playing chicken."

"What can I do about it?" asked Eve.

Top Catty-gory No. 2: **The Chicken Cat**

"All you need to do is use the following Flow Chart," I said.

We walked off down the street. Eve was looking behind her all the time.

"What are you looking for?" I asked.

"To see if the Flow Chart is following," she explained.

"Well, of course it is! It wouldn't be a *following* Flow Chart if it wasn't, would it?'

THE FOLLOWING FLOW CHART ON HOW TO HANDLE THE CHICKEN CAT.

Show your cat this picture of a cat and a chicken:

Cat   Chicken

Tell your cat: "See, there's no way a cat is like a chicken."

DOES YOUR CAT SAY: "Of course, you're right! What a foolish Kitty I have been! I'm not a chicken cat." → YES → YE-HAH! Result! Your cat will never run in front of your brother's skateboard again.

NO

DOES YOUR CAT SAY: "What about Billy Bonegrinder then?" → YES → Your cat has a point. There's no way Billy Bonegrinder looks like a member of the human race, even though he is.

Member of Human Race   Billy Bonegrinder

Tell your cat: "OK, then. If you're a chicken you can lay me an egg for breakfast every day."

DOES YOUR CAT SAY: → → →

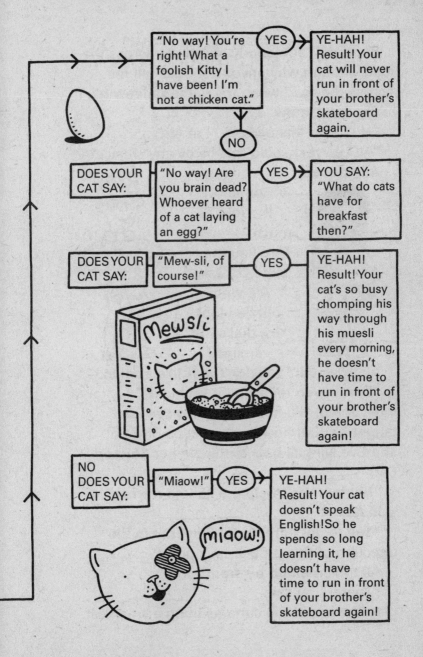

"No way! You're right! What a foolish Kitty I have been! I'm not a chicken cat."

YES

YE-HAH! Result! Your cat will never run in front of your brother's skateboard again.

NO

DOES YOUR CAT SAY:

"No way! Are you brain dead? Whoever heard of a cat laying an egg?"

YES

YOU SAY: "What do cats have for breakfast then?"

DOES YOUR CAT SAY:

"Mew-sli, of course!"

YES

YE-HAH! Result! Your cat's so busy chomping his way through his muesli every morning, he doesn't have time to run in front of your brother's skateboard again!

NO
DOES YOUR CAT SAY:

"Miaow!"

YES

YE-HAH! Result! Your cat doesn't speak English! So he spends so long learning it, he doesn't have time to run in front of your brother's skateboard again!

miaow!

Suddenly, somebody called me across the road. Though why anyone should call me Across-the-road when my name's Meow-gli, I really don't know.

"Hi!" said this person. "I'm Ali."

"Ali Lewyer, would that be by any chance?" Ali nodded.

"Somehow, I thought as much," I replied. "Are you the cat expert?" asked Ali, with a puzzled look. "Yes, that's me," I smiled.

Ali frowned. "You don't *look* like a cat ex—"

"Don't even *think* about saying it!" I interrupted. "I'll have you know I've just taught Kit Katt how to handle his Bird Cat and Eve Ningall how to handle her Chicken Cat!"

"Bet you can't help me handle *my* cat," said Ali.

"You're on!" I replied. "Point me in the direction of this problematic puss!'

Ali took me into his front room.

"There!" he said.

At the top of the curtains hung a small cat.

"That's Lopy."

"Lopy?"

"It's short for Envelopy. We called her that, 'cos she's always getting stuck up, like an envelope."

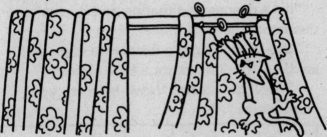

"Where does she get stuck up?" I asked.

"The curtains," replied Ali. "And the trouble is, every time she gets stuck up the curtains, I have to go and get Dad's ladder from the shed and fetch her down. And as Lopy runs up the curtains about 60 times a day and it takes ages to get her down, I don't get any time to do things I want to do like ring my mates or watch telly."

"What you have in Lopy," I replied, "is a cat who thinks she's a spider."

Top Catty-gory No. 3: **The Spider Cat**

"Very interesting and all that," said Ali, "but how do I handle her?"

"It's a desperate situation and it calls for a desperate measure."

"Oh, I haven't got a desperate measure," said Ali, "but I have got a tape measure."

"That'll do," I said. "Now, here are your instructions."

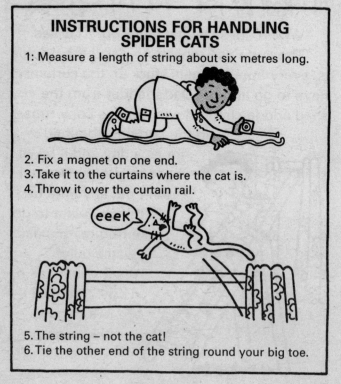

INSTRUCTIONS FOR HANDLING SPIDER CATS

1: Measure a length of string about six metres long.

2. Fix a magnet on one end.
3. Take it to the curtains where the cat is.
4. Throw it over the curtain rail.

5. The string – not the cat!
6. Tie the other end of the string round your big toe.

7. Sit down on the sofa and watch the telly and ring your mates.

8. Wait for your Spider cat to run up the curtains.

9. Your cat's name tag attaches itself to the magnet on the end of the string.

10. Raise your foot slowly.

11. No! Your other foot – the one with the big toe that has the string tied round it!

12. No! Not both legs together!

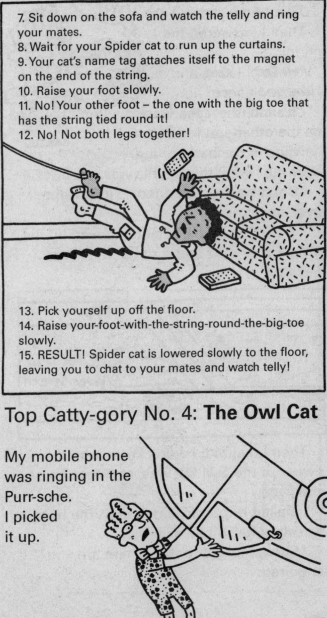

13. Pick yourself up off the floor.

14. Raise your-foot-with-the-string-round-the-big-toe slowly.

15. RESULT! Spider cat is lowered slowly to the floor, leaving you to chat to your mates and watch telly!

Top Catty-gory No. 4: **The Owl Cat**

My mobile phone was ringing in the Purr-sche. I picked it up.

That's how strong I am.

Then I answered the phone.

"Hello?" I said. "Meow-gli here."

I couldn't hear the voice on the other end for all the howling in the background. I knew just what the trouble was: an Owl Cat.

"Don't worry," I shouted. "I'll be right over."

I drove the Purr-sche at top speed up the M7, down the A7 and through the River Severn.

Then I realized: I didn't know who the owner of the Owl Cat was, or where he or she lived.

I dialled ringback. Fortunately, the howling wasn't quite so bad as before.

"Sorry, I forgot to ask, where are you?" I enquired.

"In the kitchen," came the reply.

"No! I meant what's your address?"

"Tenby Gardens."

I knew Tenby Gardens well. It was next to Elevenby Gardens. I drove straight there.

A worried-looking girl opened the door.

"I'm so glad you managed to get here," she said.

"So am I," I said.

"I'm having such trouble with my cat, Leda. Oh, by the way, I'm Jilly. Jilly Really."

"Fancy that," I replied. "I'm Really Chilly."

"I'm not surprised, wearing that naff fake leopard-skin leotard," retorted Jilly. She looked at me, hard. "Are you sure you're a cat expert? Only you don't look like—"

"Enough!" I shouted. "Take me to your Leda!"

Leda the cat was in Jilly's bedroom, howling her head off.

"She sounds like Worstlife on a bad day," I said.

"She's even worse at nights," explained Jilly. "Then she sounds like Worstlife on a *good* day."

"Then it's serious," I said. "I suppose you have trouble getting to sleep?"

"It's not that," said Jilly. "The real problem is I can't concentrate on reading *Smash Zits* magazine under the covers."

"Don't you mean *Smash Hits*?" I said. "The magazine that gives you full colour pictures of the boy bands who've got the biggest hits?"

"No, I mean *Smash Zits*, the magazine that gives you full colour pictures of the boy bands who've got the biggest zits," said Jilly.

"The point is, what do I do about Leda?"

"The trouble is," I explained, "Leda's 'owling because she thinks she's an Owl."

"Whatever gave her that idea?" asked Jilly.

"Something she read," I said. "You may know it. It's called *The Owl and the Pussy Cat*? It's about this owl and this cat who got married and..."

"Oh, I see," nodded Jilly. "Leda thinks she's descended from them."

"Exactly," I said. "And there's only one way you can handle your Owl Cat problem. And that is to buy half a dozen multi-packs of this special Owl Cat food."

"Whispas?"

"It's guaranteed to quieten Owl Cats' 'owling. After a bowl full of this, they'll only be able to whisper."

"What's in it, then?"

"Chicken, liver and a special kind of mince."

"What kind of mince?"

"Extra strong mints."

We watched Leda eat her bowl of Whispas. She loved it. And when she opened her mouth, instead of...

Hooowwwwwl

...we heard:

H-h-h-h-h-u-u-r-r

"Thanks Meow-gli," said Jilly.

"My pleasure," I replied. "Now, you must excuse me. I've got to go and see a boy about a cat."

The appointment I had was with Callum Mitty.

"Hello," I said. "I'm Meow-gli from Pets Resc-You. I've come about your cat."

Callum looked me up and down and I felt myself blushing.

"And before you comment on my looks," I continued, crossly, "I'll have you know that I am a proper expert."

Callum nodded. "I can see that," he said.

I frowned. "How?"

"Well perhaps not so much a proper *expert*, more like a proper *x-spurt*."

"An *x-spurt*?'

"Yes, it's another name for a cross little drip," Callum added.

a cross

little drip

I was about to tell Callum I'd rather be a little drip than a big wet nelly like he was when there was a ...

THUMP

... and a ...

MEE-OWWWWW!!!!!

... from the back garden.

"Quick! It's Cabbage!" yelled Callum.

We dashed round the back. There, by a tall garden wall was a small cat, looking very dazed.

"Oh no, Cabbage, you haven't gone and done it again!" sighed Callum.

"Excuse me for asking," I said. "But why do you call your cat Cabbage?"

"When we got him he was a tiny kitten and we were afraid our pet Rottweiler, Fang, would eat him," explained Callum. "So we called him Cabbage, 'cos Fang hates Cabbage. The trouble is, Cabbage keeps going to sleep on top of the wall and then falling off."

Top Catty-gory No. 5: **The Boa Constrictor Cat**

"Cabbage is what is technically known as a Boa Constrictor Cat," I said. "This is a cat who thinks he's a snake. And because he thinks he's a snake, he thinks he's long and thin enough to sleep on top of a wall without falling off."

"How do I handle such a problem?" asked Callum.

"Simple," I replied. "You need something at the bottom of the wall that's soft so he doesn't hurt himself and bouncy so he goes straight back up to the top of the wall again."

"My dad wouldn't let me put anything on his vegetable patch," said Callum, sadly.

"He'd let you grow vegetables there, though, wouldn't he?"

"But what vegetables would make Cabbage bounce back up on to the wall?"

"Obvious, isn't it?" I replied. "SPRING onions!"

Callum planted spring onions, and now every time Cabbage falls off the wall, he bounces straight back up again.

Callum was so grateful for my brilliant solution to his problem that he gave me a bunch of flowers. Cauliflowers. Which he'd had to dig up from his dad's vegetable patch in order to plant the spring onions.

For weeks I walked around in a daze, not noticing where I was going or anything. There was no doubt about it. My success was stunning! Particularly when I walked into lampposts.

Everyone wanted to take the next stage of the Pets Resc-You Cat Handling course: Five Useful Uses For a Cat. First of all though, I insisted they tested themselves.

How To Handle Your Cat: Stage three

Test Yourself on the Top Five Catty-gories!

Which of the following are genuine Top Catty-gories and which aren't?

1. BIRD CAT *Yes*

2. CAT-ERPILLAR *no*

3. CHICKEN CAT *Yes*

4. CAT-ALOGUE *no*

5. SPIDER CAT *Yes*

6. OCTO-PUSS *no*

7. OWL CAT *Yes*

8. CAT-AMARAN *no*

9. BOA CONSTRICTOR CAT *Yes*

ANSWERS:

1. Right!
2. Wrong. A Cat-erpillar is what a cat puts its head on to go to sleep at night.
3. Right!
4. Wrong. A Cat-alogue is a length of sawn-up tree a cat sleeps on during the day.
5. Right!
6. Wrong. An Octo-puss is a cat with eight legs.
7. Right!
8. Wrong. The Cat-amaran is a beautiful pea-green boat once used by an owl and a pussy cat to sail away in for a year and a day. It can be seen at the Maritime Museum in the Land where the Bong Tree grows.
9. Right!

Score 5 for every right answer. Score minus five for every left answer.

WHAT YOUR SCORE MEANS:

25 points   Top score – top cat!
5 points   A Cat-astrophe!
0 pints   Your cat's been at the milk again.

How To Handle Your Cat: Stage four

Five Useful Uses for a Cat

Kit Katt, Eve Ningall, Ali Lewyer and Jilly Really were all gathered at the Pets Resc-You Centre in the park.

"Where's Callum Mitty?" I asked.

"His dad's banned him from going out for a year," explained Kit.

"Why?" I asked.

" 'Cos he dug up his prize cauliflowers," said Kit.

"Oh dear," I said.

Kit nodded. "He told me the first thing he's going to do when his dad does let him out is to conduct an experiment."

"What sort of experiment?" I asked.

"He didn't go into too much detail," said Kit. "But it's going to involve your brain and a sledge hammer."

I quickly changed the subject. "Cats are useful for helping you handle grans, brothers, sisters, dads and enemies," I explained. "Now, who's got a problem with their gran?"

Eve Ningall put her hand up. Or rather, she tried to. But it was weighed down by about five hundred kilos of jumper.

"My gran knitted this," she said, glumly. "She can't convert inches into centimetres so she always gets the sizes a little wrong."

"Not so much a little wrong as a big wrong," I replied. "And why has she knitted a penguin on the front?"

"That's another thing," sighed Eve. "I asked for a *Man U* jumper, but she got confused and knitted a *Ping-U* jumper."

"You're lucky you've got a cat," I said, "because you can train Miffkins to solve your gruesome gran problem for you. And this is how you do it..."

Useful Uses for a Cat No. 1: **The Cat-on-the-lap**

Your gran is sitting in an arm chair knitting you a new jumper which is looking as if it would be a generous fit on King Kong. You distract your gran:

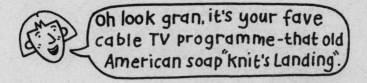

Oh look gran, it's your fave cable TV programme - that old American soap "knit's Landing".

So it is!

While your gran's attention is taken by the TV, you plonk Miffkins on her lap. Immediately, he begins to unravel the dreadful jumper!

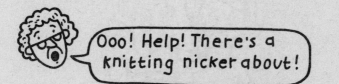

Ooo! Help! There's a knitting nicker about!

RESULT: As a result of your cat in your gran's lap, in two minutes flat the hideous jumper is no more!

WARNING!
Do not place your cat too close to the scene of the action, or he could end up with one of your gran's needles up his bottom. Even worse, he could find himself on the end of your gran's needles actually being *knitted into* the jumper!

"I've got a problem with my big brother," said Kit. "Or rather with his girlfriend. She's gross."

"Then you need to train your cat Tiddles to sort out your bothersome brother problem for you," I said. "And this is how you do it..."

Useful Uses for a Cat No. 2: **The Cat Flap**

Cats are very friendly, generous creatures, always keen to give their owners presents. Unfortunately, these presents aren't usually items that cat owners appreciate, e.g. dead mice and live frogs. Your brother's yukky girlfriend has left her Yucci bag by the front door. Put a little piece of tuna fish next to it.

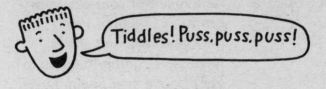

Tiddles bounds up, and sees the fish. Ever grateful, he bounds out again. Then bounds back with a present. A lovely, juicy live frog, which he proceeds to drop into Yukky Girlfriend's Yucci bag.

When your brother and his girlfriend get to the disco and she opens her bag, she says...

Eeeeeiiiikkkkk!

Now the joint really starts jumping. And so does your brother's girlfriend.

RESULT: As a result of your cat, your brother's in a flap! His girlfriend tells him she is never, ever going to come to your house ever again. Ever!

WARNING!
Make sure you tell Tiddles to lay low for a few days, because the chances are your brother's girlfriend will have asked him to provide her with a new Yucci handbag made out of cat skin.

Jilly Really was looking glum. "It's my little sister," she said.

"Aargh! Where!" screamed everyone. They started running off in all directions.

"No, no, come back!" shouted Jilly. "I don't mean my little sister is coming here, I mean my little sister is a big problem."

Once everyone had been reassured that Jilly's little sister was not in the vicinity, the Pets Resc-You Cat Handling course was able to continue.

"The thing about her," Jilly explained, "is that she's always sneaking into my room and poking about."

"Then you need to train your cat Leda to sort out your serious sister problem for you," I said. "And this is how you do it..."

Useful Uses for a Cat No. 3: **The Cat Trap**

Just before you go to school scatter a handful of cat treats over your bedroom floor. Leave your bedroom door open. Place a ball of wool by the door.

While you're at school, your cat will go walkabout, taking the ball of wool with it. But not only will your cat go walk about, it will go walk-around, walk-a-down, walk-a-through and walk-a-up.

So when your little
sister comes home
from school and
sneaks into your room
she crashes headlong
over the web of wool
that your cat has left!

RESULT: As a result of your cat's trap,
your little sister never dares
enter your bedroom again!

WARNING!

Do not attempt the Cat Trap on the third
Tuesday on any month with "r" in it, which
are the days your mum goes into your room
to hoover up. Or else you could find yourself
in the soup and your cat could find itself in
the hoover.

"I've got a problem with my dad," said Ali
Lewyer, "he's always having a doze."

"My dad's pretty dozy, too," agreed Kit.

"Yes, but my dad's always asleep when I need him to play WWF wrestling with me," added Ali.

"Then you need to train your cat Lopy to sort out your desperate dad problem for you," I said. "And this is how you do it..."

Useful Uses for a Cat No. 4: **The Cat Nap**

It's time for your dad to play WWF wrestling with you. But, as usual, he is asleep. So, as usual, is your cat. Gently lift the sleeping cat on to your dad's knee. Then shout:

Your cat thinks there's a dog in the room and waking suddenly, digs his claws into your dad's knees.

RESULT: As a result of your cat having a nap your dad is awake and ready to play WWF wrestling with you!

WARNING!
Make sure your cat doesn't see you going "woof, woof", otherwise you could find yourself cat-wrestling instead of WWF wrestling.

"You said our cats could help us handle our enemies," said Jilly.

"That's right," I replied. "Does anyone here have trouble with Public Enemy Number One, Killer Sharkey?"

"Yes!" chorussed everyone.

"Yes!" echoed a voice behind me.

I spun round, went dizzy and fell over. When I got up, I saw I was facing a mum-type figure.

Killer's a rotten rascal,
I can't handle him at all.

"And who are you?" I asked.

"I'm his mum, of course!"

"Mrs Sharkey, have you got a cat?" I asked. "Course we have! Haven't you ever seen him? He's always in the chemist's," replied Mrs Sharkey.

"Oh, you mean Puss in Boots!" I said.

"Well, you need to train your Puss to sort out your shocking Sharkey problem for you," I said. "And this is how you do it..."

Useful Uses for a Cat No. 5: **The Cat Scrap**

1. Lure cat up apple tree with a saucer of milk.
2. Wait for cat to go to sleep.
3. Rig up pulley system with toy mouse.

Then shout:

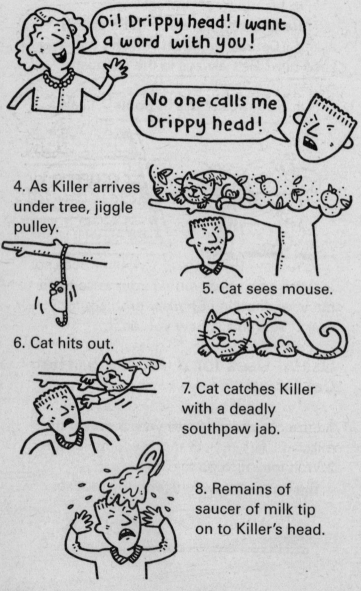

Oi! Drippy head! I want a word with you!

No one calls me Drippy head!

4. As Killer arrives under tree, jiggle pulley.

5. Cat sees mouse.

6. Cat hits out.

7. Cat catches Killer with a deadly southpaw jab.

8. Remains of saucer of milk tip on to Killer's head.

WARNING!
If you're not Mrs Sharkey and Killer does set his mum on to you, you could find yourself getting an 'orrible ear bashing.

The Pets Resc-You Cat Handling was over. Kit Katt, Eve Ningall, Ali Lewyer, Jilly Really and Mrs Sharkey all had their problems solved.
   And what about you, dear reader? And you, cheap reader? Do the check list on the next page. to see how much you have learnt about handling your cat.

*You should only say this if your name is Mrs Sharkey.

How To Handle Your Cat: Stage five

The Meow-gli Cat Handling Checklist

Mix 'n' match the following people with the names of the cats who handled them and what people said when they'd been handled:

| 1. Eve Ningall's gran | a: Tiddles | i: I'm getting my mum on to you! |
| 2. Kit Katt's big brother's girlfriend | b: Puss | ii: Eeeeeiiiikkkkkk! |

3. Jilly Really's little sister	c: Lopy	iii: Yee-ooowwww!
4. Ali Lewyer's dad	d: Leda	iv: Oooo-ow!!!!
5. Mrs Sharkey's Killer	e: Miffkins	v: Ooo! Help!

ANSWERS:
1. e v, 2. a ii, 3. d iv, 4. c iii, 5. b i

How To Handle
Your Dog

Scholastic Children's Books,
Commonwealth House, 1-19 New Oxford Street,
London WC1A 1NU, UK
a division of Scholastic Ltd
London ~ New York ~ Toronto ~ Sydney ~ Auckland
Mexico City ~ New Delhi ~ Hong Kong

First published in the UK by Scholastic Ltd, 2001

ISBN 0 439 99222 2

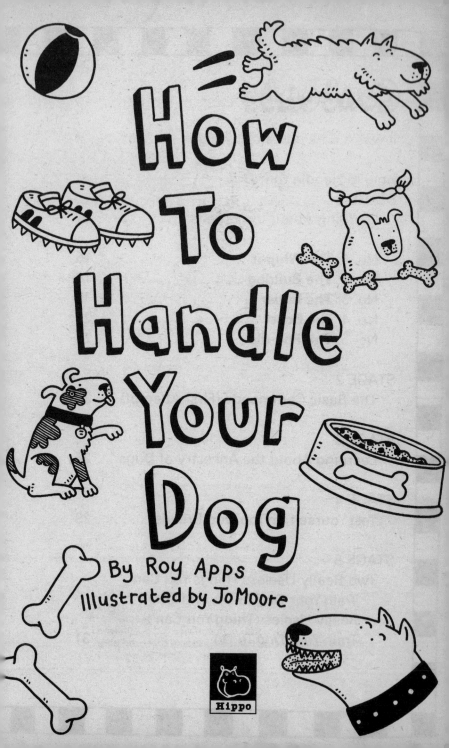

Contents

STAGE 8

It was a dark and stormy night...
The wind howled in the trees. The trees
howled in the wind. Thunder roared and
lightning struck. It was the sort of night you
wouldn't even take a dog out in.

So I took the dog I'd taken out in the rain in
out of the rain and went into the kitchen. I
was opening a tin of jellied liver and kidneys
for my dog when the
phone started to ring.
I picked it up.
"Hello?" I said.
"Squelloop ...
globglurpgloosh..." came
the reply. Then I realized I'd
put the tin of jellied liver
and kidneys to my ear, instead of the phone.
I put the phone to my ear. "Hello, who's
there?"
"Get those horrible slimy chunks of dog
food off of my handset," screeched my
phone. Most people have an Answerphone. I,

7

however, have got an Answerbackphone.*

"A couple of messages have been left on me for you," continued my Answerbackphone. "And it's about time you heard them."

There was a blip and a beep and a burp. Then my Answerbackphone played me back the first message:

Hello..? Can you come as soon as possible! I'm having terrible trouble with my dog! I'm Soph Rantic! Please, please come quicky!

There was something about this message which suggested it might be urgent, though I couldn't quite put my finger on it. Mainly because I was still trying to open the can of dog food.

I dashed out of the house, leapt into the van and was knocking at Soph Rantic's door before you could say

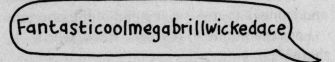

Fantasticoolmegabrillwickedace

The reason I was at the door of the person

*Those of you who have read *How To Handle Your Cat* will know this.

who'd called me before you could say
Fantasticoolmegabrillwickedace was that
Soph Rantic lived next door.

Soph opened the door.

"You left an urgent message for me –
about some terrible trouble you were having
with your dog," I began.

You took your time

"I'll have you know that I raced round here
as soon as I got your message. It only took
me five seconds."

"That's as may be. But I left my urgent
message six weeks ago last Saturday!"

"Are you going to let me in?" I said,
getting in a huff. "It's a dark and stormy night
out here."

"All right."

So I got out of my huff and went in.

Now you may wonder why Soph next door
had called me in to sort out the problem with
her dog.* In fact, if you've already read the
other side of this book, you'll want to know

*If you don't wonder why Soph next door had called me in to sort out the
problem with her dog, then skip the next bit. And if you can't skip, just jump
instead.

why a *cat* expert like me is racing about sorting out dogs. Well, the truth is, I am one very special person. Or rather, like Bratman* and Souperman** I am *two* very special persons. And one of the very special sort of persons I am is:***

LUKE DOGWALKER
SOLE PROPRIETOR: PETS RESC-YOU

WE RESCUE YOU FROM YOUR PETS
24-HOUR ANSWERBACKPHONE

I followed Soph in.

"How did you know it was me who left the message?" she asked.

"There's only one girl called Soph Rantic in this town," I replied.

"There's two actually," said Soph. "There's another girl called Soph Rantic who lives in Dracula Avenue."

*See *How To Handle Your Brother/Sister*
**See *How To Handle Your Friends/Enemies*
***If you've read *How To Handle Your Cat*, you'll know what the other very special sort of person I am is. If you haven't you won't, but you soon will when you do (turn this book over and read *How To Handle Your Cat* that is).

"Yes, but *she* hasn't got a dog. Now stop arguing and tell me what the problem with your dog is."

"He went off down the road after a cat and never came back."

"Oh Soph," I said, genuinely concerned. "When did this happen?"

"Six weeks ago last Saturday – when I called you!"

"I'm sure he'll come home," I said.

Suddenly, there was crash at the door and a rocket on four legs powered by at least half a dozen turbo-charged engines launched itself at my chest. Then the rocket knocked me over. Next, the rocket knocked me under, through and sideways. Finally it put his paws on my shoulders and started licking my face.

"Oh Bonzo, poppet," simpered Soph. "You are a rascal!"

I was *agog*. Unlike Bonzo, who obviously, was *a dog*.

Agog   A dog

"I thought you said your dog was missing!" I yelled, trying to stop Bonzo from sandpapering the inside of my ear with his tongue.

"He was."

"Well, he's not missing now!"

"He was missing six weeks ago last Saturday when I called you and left a message on your Answerbackphone."

"So, when did he come back home?"

"Six weeks ago last Sunday."

I turned to go. "I see," I said, tersely, wiping dog gob from my chin.

"You've called me all the way round here on a dark and stormy night and there isn't even a problem. Good night."

"But I *do* have a problem with my dog," Soph gushed.

"You're not the only one," I muttered from underneath Bonzo. "Now, can you call your dog OFF!"

"Off? That's a bit of a daft name for a dog, isn't it?" said Soph. "Anyway, his name's Bonzo. Here Bonzo!"

Using my stomach as a launch pad, Bonzo propelled himself across the other side of the room.

"May I suggest," I said, "that you go out and buy a copy of the number one advice book on dog handling. It's called..."

"I'll do that," said Soph.

"Cool," I said. And went home to get some sleep.

How To Handle Your Dog: Stage one

Learning About Top Dog Breeds

Two days later Soph called me round to her house.

"I bought the book," she said. "But I've got a real problem with it."

"Did you read and thoroughly digest it?" I asked.

"No I didn't read it, but Bonzo thoroughly digested it. You see, I left it on the table. And Bonzo ate it!"

"I can't imagine he found eating a book very tasty."

"No," agreed Soph, "that's why he mixed it with a plate of left-over curry, a pair of my brother's smelly football socks, a dishcloth and a cactus plant.

This is a problem with Bonzo. He just puts his front paws up on the table and eats whatever is on there.

Just what kind of dog does a thing like that?"

"A Top Breed of Dog called a Whip-it," I replied.

Soph frowned. "You mean he's like Walter Winterbottom in Year 3 who wears a balaclava for football?"

"No, no. Walter Winterbottom isn't a whip-it. He's a Wimp-it."

a whip-it   a wimp-it

"It's very confusing," sighed Soph.

"Let me tell you some facts about Whip-its, then," I suggested.

Top Breed of Dog No. 1: **The Whip-it**

an ordinary dog's insides

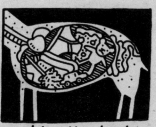

a whip-it's insides

Good name to call a Whip-it:

Fried-Do

Not-so-good name to call a Whip-it:

Finn

Soph nodded. "I see," she said. "Do you think you'd be able to teach me how to handle Bonzo?"

"Of course! No problem," I replied. "I'll teach you all the basic commands. Come along with me to my Pets Resc-You Centre. It's only a short walk."

Unfortunately, on hearing me say "walk", Bonzo leapt up, raced across the room and knocked me flat on my face again.

"I've changed my opinion," I said. "Bonzo isn't a pedigree Whip-it. He's a cross. Though not half as cross as I am."

Soph pulled Bonzo off me.

"Bonzo is part-Whip-it and part-Bulldog."

"He's not a bald dog. He's quite hairy!" retorted Soph, tetchily.

"I said *Bull*dog, not *bald* dog," I replied. "The kind of dog that's always charging at you like a runaway bull."

a bald dog   a bulldog

"And is the Bulldog another Top Breed?" asked Soph.

"Indeed it is," I replied. "And here are the important facts about the bulldog breed."

Top Breed of Dog No. 2: **The Bulldog**

an ordinary dog coming towards you

a bulldog coming towards you

Good name to call a Bulldog:

Not-so-good name to call a Bulldog:

Fido

We were just about to cross the road, when something shot past us, taking its owner with it.

"Did you see that?" I asked Soph.

"No," she replied.

"That's because that was a breed of dog known as a terrier," I explained. "Terriers are always tearing about the place."

Top Breed of Dog No. 3: **The Terrier**

Good name to call a terrier:

Doesn't really matter what you call it, because terriers never come they only

Goooooooo !!!!

Not-so-good name for a terrier:

ROVER (The best Rover can only do about 120. Terriers go at least twice that speed.)

We turned a corner and came across Lewis Lennox. His dog was fighting him.

"Now Lewis's dog is the Top Breed of dog us experts call a Boxer," I said.

"I rather thought it might be," replied Soph.

Top Breed of Dog No. 4: **The Boxer**

Ordinary Dog

Boxer

Good name for a Boxer:

PRINCE: Because his paw *prints* are likely to be all over you.

Not-so-good name for a Boxer:

PRINCESS: Can you imagine calling Lennox Lewis "Princess"?

Walking past the florist's, we saw Meg Affone and her dog. Meg's cheeks were like the school library copy of "Harry Potter", i.e. well read.

"What's she looking so embarrassed about?" asked Soph. "Has she done something she shouldn't have?"

"*She* hasn't," I replied. "But her dog has. Right outside the posh florist's. I'm afraid Meg's got a Top Breed of dog us experts call a Poo-dle.* So called, because they're always doing a poo in the most embarrassing and most public places.

Top Breed of Dog No. 5: **Poo-dle**

Good name to call a Poo-dle:

It's best if you don't call them. That way you can pretend they're not your dog.

Ordinary dog with owner

Poodle with owner

*Not to be confused with the breed of dog which always wees where it shouldn't. These dogs are known, of course, as PEE-KINESE.

How To Handle Your Dog: Stage two

The Basic Commands (First Attempt)

The Luke Dogwalker Pets Resc-You Centre was a large green, open space, just like a park. There was a good reason for this: It *was* a park. Bonzo ran into the park ahead of us.

In fact, he was there on the dot of nine o'clock. And when I say on the dot of nine o'clock, I mean on the dot of nine o'clock. Bonzo had chased a cat up the clock tower and was sitting perched on the hour hand right on the dot next to the nine, barking up at the cat who was sitting on the minute hand.

"Oh," cried Soph, "we've got to save Bonzo. What shall we do?"

"Call Pets Rescue," I said.

"You *are* Pets Rescue," snapped Soph.

"I'm not, I'm Pets Resc-*You*," I replied.

"Completely different thing."

Bonzo's weight was slowly pushing the hour hand back. It was now six o'clock.

"He must be the first dog to have travelled back in time," I observed.

"We've gotta save him!" yelled Soph. "If he falls he'll really hurt himself!"

"I'll go up and chat to him. Try to persuade him not to jump."

"Hurry!" urged Soph.

"No," I advised. "I don't want to panic him. I'm not going to run up to the clock tower, I'll just walk, calmly."

Unfortunately, on hearing me say "walk", Bonzo's ears pricked up and he leapt off the clock face. Even more unfortunately (for me, at any rate) I was directly under the clock tower. He landed straight on top of me. He wasn't hurt at all.

How To Handle Your Dog: Stage three

Learning About The Ancestry of Dogs

Luckily, my injuries weren't serious and I was out of hospital in a couple of months.

Soph and Bonzo came to see me while I was recovering and I taught Soph about the ancestry of dogs.

"Dogs evolved from wolves," I explained. "Do you know about wolves?"

"Of course I do," snapped Soph. "They're a naff first division football team."

I ignored her. "From the original ancient pack of wolves, there evolved two distinct types of dogs; *werewolves*, which are really scary wild dogs and *weirdwolves*, which are really lairy pet dogs."

A really scarey
wild dog

A really lairy
pet dog

"What about sheepdogs?" asked Soph.

"They're slightly different," I explained.
"Sheepdogs are obviously descended from a
cross between a sheep and a dog called a
werewool. Let me draw you a diagram:"

DOGS' ANCESTRAL TREE

WEREWOLF   WIERDWOLF   WEREWOOL

Hound of the   Hound of the   Lassie
Baskervilles   Basketvilles

Scarey dogs   Pet dogs   Sheepdogs

"So, Bonzo is a descendant of a weirdwolf?" frowned Soph.

"Got it in one," I replied.

"So has Bonzo," said Soph.

I turned and saw Bonzo with his paws up on my bedside cabinet, scoffing all the favourite food my friends had brought me* *and* all the un-favourite food my enemies had brought in for me**.

When I got back on my feet, I went next door to see Soph. The change in Bonzo was remarkable. Not once did he charge at me. He stayed quite still on the floor.

"Amazing," I said. 'It's like he's glued to the floor."

"He *is* glued to the floor," replied Soph. "He whipped a tube of super glue from the kitchen table."

*i.e. chocolate eggs, maltesers, white chocolate.
**i.e. hard boiled eggs, a jar of olives disguised as maltesers, a bar of soap carved in the shape of a slab of white chocolate.

My plans for training Bonzo had come unstuck – which was more than could be said for Bonzo.

"Never mind, at least now I know everything there is to know about the Top Dog Breeds," said Soph.

"But *do* you?" I replied.

"I *think* so," frowned Soph.

"Thinking so isn't good enough. I must ask you to take the following test."

"Go on, then," said Soph.

"OK," I said. " 'I-ask-you-to-take-the-following-test.' "

THE FOLLOWING TEST ... OR...

How To Handle Your Dog: Stage four

Test Yourself on Top Dog Breeds

1. If you had two dogs who were always woofing things off the table what would you call them?
   A: A couple of Whip-its
   B: A Pair of Nickers

2. Which of the following best describes a dog that is always charging you?
   A: A Bulldog
   B: A Bulldozer
   C: A Bull-it

3. What would you do if you met a boxer in a dark alley?
   A: Shout "I've seen tougher looking chihuahuas!"
   B: Panic
   C: Run

4. Which of these animals always seems to be doing its business in public places?
   A: Winnie the Pooh
   B: A Poo-dle

ANSWERS:

1. A: 10 points
   B: 5 points. A pair of knickers is the sort of thing a Whip-it likes to whip.

2. A: 10 points
   B: 5 points. Pretty close – though not as close as a Bulldog gets. And even when it is not close it isn't pretty.
   C: 5 points. A Bulldog is faster than a bull-it.

3. A: 2 pints – that's about the amount of blood you'll lose when the boxer nips your shin.
   B: 5 points
   C: 10 points

4. A: 0 points
   B: 10 points

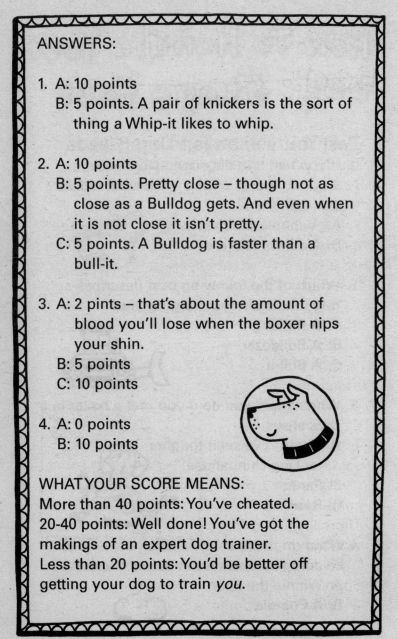

WHAT YOUR SCORE MEANS:
More than 40 points: You've cheated.
20-40 points: Well done! You've got the makings of an expert dog trainer.
Less than 20 points: You'd be better off getting your dog to train *you*.

How To Handle Your Dog: Stage five

Two really useless things you can train your dog to do and one really useless thing you can't train your dog to do

A few weeks later I was out for a walk when a hurricane struck. Hurricane Bonzo: out for a walk with Soph. I was bowled over to see her. Right over. On my bottom.

"Oh, I am glad I bumped into you," said Soph. Although technically it wasn't Soph who had bumped into me, but Bonzo.

"The thing is, I'd really like to be able to train Bonzo to do something useful."

"Actually, I'm just off to Crwofts, the Top Dog Show," I said.

"Why don't you come along with me? There'll be all sorts of working dogs there."

"Would you like me to pick you up?" asked Soph.

"Why, have you got a car?"

"No! I meant would you like me to pick you up off the pavement?"

"Thank you," I said.

Half an hour later, Soph and I sat in the front row at Crwofts. A group of dogs sat down in the ring. They had whistles rounds their necks and they carried green flags in their front paws."

"Are they waiting for their trainer?" enquired Soph.

"No," I replied. "They're waiting for their *train*. These are *guard* dogs."

"I didn't realize that dogs worked as guards on trains," said Soph.

"Oh yes, they're very common. Especially on one particular line."

Soph winced. "That wouldn't be the Barking to Kennelworth Line, by any chance, would it?" she asked.

I nodded.

"I had a dreadful feeling it might be," she said.

"Of course, they're also a familiar sight on the London UndergrrrHound."

Suddenly, everyone started to leave their seats. "Quick," I said. "Time to go!"

Into the arena bounded a pack of dogs, their noses twitching.

"These are the sniffer dogs," I explained. "Trained to sniff people in all the most embarrassing places."

I raced out of Crwoft's with Soph, as the Sniffer dogs began rubbing their noses all over the people who hadn't been able to get out in time.

As we walked home, Soph said, "Training Bonzo to become a guard dog or a sniffer dog doesn't seem very useful to me. Couldn't we train him to do something really helpful, like being a Guide Dog?"

I shook my head. "Training a dog to become a Guide Dog is very difficult," I said.

"Is it?" asked Soph.

"Of course it is. I mean, have you ever tried getting a dog to wear a blue blouse, a beret and a natty scarf?"

Soph sighed. "Isn't there anything useful at all that Bonzo could do?"

"Can't he work your video for you?"

Soph shook her head. "Should he be able to?"

"All dogs ought to be able to work the video for you," I replied. "That's why videos have a paws button."

"And there's really nothing else I could train Bonzo to do?"

"Not really," I said. "Not unless you have problems with your mum, dad, sister, teacher or enemies."

"Did you say not unless you have problems with your mum, dad, sister, teacher or enemies?"

I checked back to the previous sentence. "It rather looks as if I did."

"Yes, I do have problems with all those people!" yelled Soph excitedly. "Particularly with my big sister."

"Your big sister need be a problem no more," I exclaimed. "What's the point in having a dog, if they can't help you handle all those people in your life who cause you so much grief? All you need is one dog-handling command."

"Which is?" asked Soph.

"I'll pop round to your house after school tomorrow," I said. "Everything will be explained then."

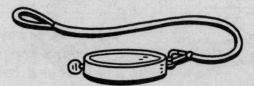

How To Handle Your Dog: Stage Six

Four pretty useful dog-handling commands, one ugly useful dog-handling command and one really ugly useful dog-handling uniform

THE REALLY UGLY USEFUL DOG-HANDLING UNIFORM
Next day, I arrived at Soph's house dressed for dog-handling:

FULL-FACE VISOR

HARD HAT

In case dog leaps off clock tower (see page 24)

For when dog licks your face (after it's been drinking scummy pond water).

SPARE ARMS

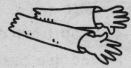

It's a good idea to have a couple of spare arms, because your dog is bound to pull your two originals out of their sockets when he races off.

SACK OF DOG TREATS

To tempt dog back when it runs off.

50 METRES OF LASSO

For when the sack of dog treats run out.

BREAD KNIFE

For cutting the lasso after dog has wrapped it round your legs.

THICK PADDING

SPIKED SHOES

To get some sort of grip when dog tries to pull you over.

So you don't get a sore bottom when dog h<u>a</u>s pulled you over.

As well as Soph and Bonzo, there were four other owners and their dogs: Wally with his Collie Molly; Lottie with her Scottie Snotty; her mate Wayne with his Great Dane Shane and Ed Banger with Jaws.

Wayne was first to speak.

"Aaaaaargh!" he said. Mainly because Ed Banger's Jaws* had just bitten his bottom.

Then Soph explained the problem with her big sister.

"She won't let me borrow her natty jacket to wear to the school disco."

Lottie, Wally and Ed gasped in outrage. Wayne gasped in pain. Jaws had bitten him on the bottom again.

"Bonzo can sort out this suffering-sister problem for you," I said. "All you need to do is to teach him to 'Fetch'."

Pretty Useful Dog-Handling Command No. 1: **FETCH!**

After a bit of practice, Soph showed Bonzo a picture of her big sister's natty jacket in a mail-order catalogue.

"Fetch!" she said.

Bonzo bounded off.

fetch!

---

*When I say Ed Banger's Jaws, I mean Jaws his dog, not jaws his teeth.

Suddenly, there was the sound of screaming and shouting outside. I looked up and saw Bonzo bounding into the room with Soph's sister's natty jacket!

"Yee-hah! Success!" I yelled.

Then I looked up again. The good news was that yes, Bonzo did have Soph's big sister's natty jacket safely in his jaws. The bad news was that Soph's big sister was wearing it.

"What do we do now?" asked Soph.
"Learn another command," I said.
"What command?" asked Soph.

RUN FOR IT!

Half an hour later, we stopped running.
"I've got to get home," said Wally.

"What's the hurry?" asked Lottie.

"It's my dad," explained Wally. "I'm terrified he's going to see my new Mindblaster CD-Rom, I haven't even dared play with it yet."

"Don't you think he'll approve of it?" I asked.

"No, it's not that. He'll 'borrow' it for his own computer," sighed Wally. "And you know dads. Once they 'borrow' something, you never get it back from them."

"Mollie your Collie can sort out this dodgy-dad problem for you," I said.

"Are you sure?" asked Wally doubtfully.

"Sure as my name's Duke Logwalker," I replied.

"Oh good," said Wally.

"Er ... your name isn't Duke Logwalker, it's Luke Dogwalker," said Soph.

I ignored her. She's so picky, that girl.

Pretty Useful Dog-Handling Command No. 2: **SIT!**

We were all in Wally's bedroom. "All you need to do is to teach Mollie the Collie to 'Sit'. Being a big dog, she can then sit on anything you like and hide it from your dad's prying eyes."

Wally taught Mollie the Collie to sit. Not before time either, because there was a tap on the door.

"It's my dad!" hissed Wally.

"Why did he want to put a tap on the door, wouldn't it have been better for him to have put it on the bath or the sink?" I asked in a whisper.

"Quick! Hide!" said Wally.

Lottie and her Scottie Snotty and Soph and Bonzo hid in the wardrobe. Wayne and his Great Dane Shane and Ed Banger and Jaws hid under the bed. I hid *in* the bed.

Wally's dad came in.

"Hi Wal," he said, in a very suspicious manner. "Seen about the new Mindblaster CD-Rom?"

Wally nodded.

"Thought you might have bought it," said Wally's dad.

All the time, he was looking around Wally's desk. Wally's Mindblaster CD-Rom was on the floor by his feet! Would he spot it? Wally had to act, and act quickly.

"Sit!" he commanded.

Straight away Wally's dad sat. On the bed. Unfortunately, of course, I was hiding in the bed.

"Actually, I was talking to Mollie," said Wally. "Sit!"

Mollie sat. On Wally's Mindblaster CD-Rom! Brilliant.

"You won't find a copy of Mindblaster in here, Dad," said Wally, with a smile.

"Pity," said Wally's dad. "I was looking forward to a good, long – arghhhhh!"

Suddenly, Wally's dad leapt up off the bed – which was good news for me – and hopped about on one leg. This was hardly surprising, as Bonzo had just nicked one of his slippers off his foot.

There's a dog under your bed!

"Wrong, Dad, there's two dogs under my bed – and two more in the wardrobe."

We slipped out of the house before you could say "Slipper".

Fortunately, Bonzo dropped Wally's dad's slipper. Unfortunately, he dropped it in their pond.

Half an hour later, Ed Banger started moaning. "All this running about is tiring me out!"

"Did I say learning to handle your dog would be easy?" I replied.

"Come round to my place for a Coke," suggested Wayne.

So we did.

We were just about to leave Wayne's house, when his mum burst into the kitchen.

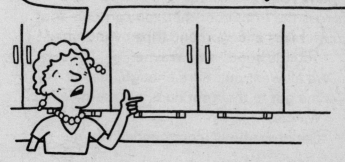

"Sounds like you've got a problem with your mum," said Lottie.

"Yes, but Shane can sort it out. All you have to do is—"

"Learn one simple command?" asked Wayne.

"However did you guess?" I asked.

Pretty Useful Dog-Handling Command No. 3: **GET DOWN, BOY!**

"What is the command?" asked Wayne.

"Get down, boy!" I answered. "What you do is this: you creep out of the house. Your mum appears behind you and tells you to get up to your room with the hoover and dustbin sacks.

Wayne nodded.

"You pretend not to have heard her," I continued. "Then you say 'Get down boy!' Shane your Great Dane flops down right across the front door mat. You carry on. Your mum races after you and trips over Shane!"

"Sounds good," said Wayne.

We all went out. Sure enough, just as Wayne got to the front door, his mum yelled:

"Wayne!"

"Get down boy!" commanded Wayne.

The good news was Shane the Great Dane flopped down on the doormat, just as Wayne had commanded. The bad news was that Wayne was *behind* Shane. He fell over on top of Shane and his mum fell over on top of *him*.

He was, so to speak, the filling in a dogmum sandwich.

We left Wayne to it and wandered up the road.

"Right, I've got this problem with my teacher, see," said Ed Banger, suddenly. "She's always wanting to mark my homework."

"Er ... isn't that what teachers are *for*, to mark your homework?" I ventured.

"Not with me, it ain't," replied Ed Banger. "I don't do homework – ever."

"What, you never, ever do homework?" I gasped.

"No, not never, ever, never," said Ed Banger.

"You need an excuse for not having any homework to hand in," I suggested. "So you need to train Jaws to sort out this tantalizing teacher problem for you."

I looked at Jaws' massive fangs. "Er ... is he obedient?" I said.

"Not half," said Ed Banger. "Watch."

I watched.

"Jaws! 'Ere boy!" said Ed Banger.

Immediately Jaws leapt up at me, knocking me over.

"That's right, Jaws. 'Ere boy!"

Immediately Jaws started biting bits off my left ear.

"See," laughed Ed Banger, triumphantly. "He does exactly what I tell him!"

"You told him to come here and he didn't come!" I complained, bitterly.

"No, I told him 'ear', so he bit your ear," explained Ed Banger.

"Do you want me to tell you how to handle Jaws so he can sort out your tantalizing teacher problem or not?" I muttered.

"Yeah, all right," shrugged Ed Banger.

Pretty Useful Dog-Handling Command No. 4: **EAT UP, BOY!**

I took a handful of doggie treats from my pocket.

"You'll need to mix these with your homework," I said. "Then you give the command: 'Eat up, boy!' So when your teacher says 'Where's your homework, Edwin?' you can say 'Dog ate it, Miss!'"

"Supposing Ed's teacher asks to see his dog?" reasoned Lottie.

"I think if Ed shows her a picture of Jaws, she'll think better of it," I replied.

Ed took the doggie treats from me and opened his school bag. "Eat up boy!" he commanded.

Jaws ate.

Then I noticed bits of metal, bolts, screws and lengths of string hanging from his mouth.

"What's that?"

I asked Ed.

"My homework," smiled Ed. "My science homework. We had to finish this model to do with levers and pullies."

I groaned. "When I suggested you command Jaws to eat your homework, I thought we were talking about a homework *book*!" I said.

"No, that wouldn't have worked," explained Ed. "Jaws doesn't like paper."

Fortunately, Jaws seemed none the worse after his metallic meal. He gave a gigantic burp and carried on walking.

"He does tend to bolt his food down a bit," said Ed.

"He tends to bolt his bolt down, as well," I observed.

"Mr Dogwalker," said Lottie, "supposing you've got this problem with an 'enemy'."

"Tell me what the problem is," I suggested.

"The problem is that she's walking straight towards us," said Lottie.

I looked up and found I was staring at a really ugly face. Then I realized I was looking in a car wing mirror.

I looked up again and saw Felicity Foulmouth coming towards us.

"Your Scottie Snottie can sort her out," I told Lottie. "All we've got to do is to teach Snottie to 'Heel!' Then he'll bite Felicity Foulmouth on the heel. Right. I'll keep Felicity Foulmouth talking, while you get on with training Snottie."

Ugly Useful Dog-Handling Command No. 1: **HEEL!**

As Felicity Foulmouth approached she called out,

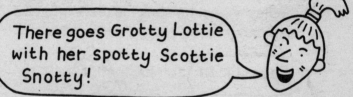

There goes Grotty Lottie with her spotty Scottie Snotty!

"Hey, punk," I said. "Nobody calls my friend's dog snotty."

"Thought that was the stupid animal's name," retorted Felicity Foulmouth.

Of course, she was right.

"All right, nobody calls my friend's dog snotty – except me," I said.

Lottie bounded up with Snottie the Scottie. "Heel!" commanded Lottie.

The good news was that Snottie obeyed Lottie's command and immediately sunk his teeth into a fleshy heel. The bad news was that the fleshy heel he sunk his teeth into was my heel, rather than Felicity Foulmouth's.

"Hey, I'm the only one allowed to say rude words like that!" pouted Felicity Foulmouth. "That's why my name's Felicity Foulmouth!"

And she stomped off in a huff.

"That reminds me," said Ed, "it's about time I had something to eat."

Everyone went off home for tea.

As I hobbled back home with Soph and Bonzo, Soph said, "That lesson on useful dog commands was really helpful, Luke Dogwalker. How can I ever thank you?"

"You can tell Bonzo to walk home instead of cadging a lift in my rucksack," I said.

"Come on, boy!" called Soph.

Straightaway, Bonzo leapt out of my rucksack. Unfortunately, he used the top of my head as a launch pad.

"Come along, Bonzo," said Soph. "Tea time."

"Wrong," I said. "*Test* time."

How To Handle Your Dog: Stage seven

The Luke Dogwalker Dog Handling Commands Test

Of the following Dog-Handling Commands, which are Pretty Useful Dog-Handling Commands, which are Ugly Useful Dog-Handling Commands, which are Incredibly Useful Dog-Handling Commands and which are Incredibly Useless Dog-Handling Commands? (Circle correct answer)

1. (a) SIT! Pretty Useful Ugly Useless Incredibly Useful Incredibly Useless

   (b) SPIT! Pretty Useful Ugly Useful Incredibly Useful Incredibly Useless

2. (a) GET DOWN, BOY! Pretty Useful Ugly Useful Incredibly Useful Incredibly Useless

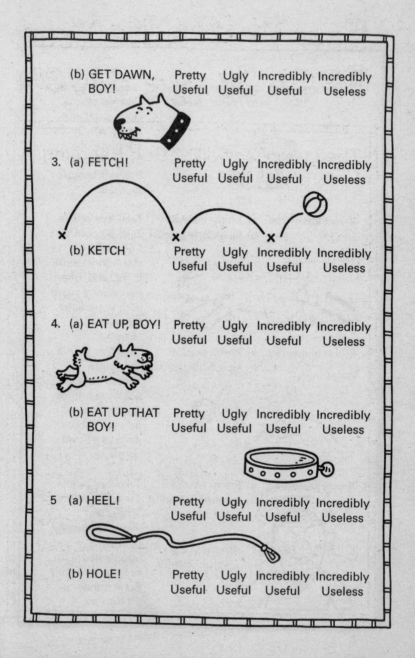

(b) GET DAWN, BOY!   Pretty Useful   Ugly Useful   Incredibly Useful   Incredibly Useless

3. (a) FETCH!   Pretty Useful   Ugly Useful   Incredibly Useful   Incredibly Useless

(b) KETCH   Pretty Useful   Ugly Useful   Incredibly Useful   Incredibly Useless

4. (a) EAT UP, BOY!   Pretty Useful   Ugly Useful   Incredibly Useful   Incredibly Useless

(b) EAT UP THAT BOY!   Pretty Useful   Ugly Useful   Incredibly Useful   Incredibly Useless

5 (a) HEEL!   Pretty Useful   Ugly Useful   Incredibly Useful   Incredibly Useless

(b) HOLE!   Pretty Useful   Ugly Useful   Incredibly Useful   Incredibly Useless

ANSWERS:
1. If you answered: a) *Pretty Useful*   Take five points.
b) *Pretty Useful*   Take no points.
Dogs can't spit.
That's why there
are none of
them playing
Premier League
football.

2. If you answered: a) *Pretty Useful*   Take five points.
b) *Incredibly Useful* Take 50 points.
This is an
incredibly useful
command when
you want a word
with your sister,
Dawn.

3. If you answered: a) *Pretty Useful*   Take five points.
b) *Incredibly Useless* No points.
"Ketch" is a
posh version of
"catch" played
by very snooty
dogs like royal
corgis.

4. If you answered: a) *Pretty Useful*   Take five points.
b) *Incredibly Useful* Take 150 points.
This is an
incredibly useful
command when
you've had it up
to here with Billy
Bone grinder or
Ed Banger.

5. If you answered: a) *Ugly Useful*   Take five points.
b) *Incredibly Useful* Take 30 points. Those huge holes your dog digs can be very useful for burying things that you suddenly find are really embarrassing to have around – like your signed S Crud 6 poster or your little brother.

YOUR SCORE: More than 20 points. Cool! You can really handle your dog, sister, brother, dad, teacher, mum, enemy.

20 points. Yes – you can really handle a hound.

10 points. Mmm ... not bad. You may not be able to handle a hound, but you can houndle a hand.

0 points. Oh dear. Perhaps you should get your dog to read this book. It wouldn't do any worse than you.

How To Handle Your Dog: Stage eight

Your Very Own Personal Dog File

YOUR DOG'S NAME

(i) WHEN IT'S BEHAVING ITSELF

.............*leroy*.............

(ii) WHEN IT'S NOT BEHAVING ITSELF

.............*leroy!*.............

BREED OF DOG (tick box)

Whip-it ☐   Bulldog ☐   Terrier ☐

Boxer ☐   Poo-dle ☐   Other (please specify)

Dobermann

Handling

1. Pretty Useful Dog-Handling Command

SIT! ☑   Date taught...........?......

DOWN BOY! ☑   Date taught...........?......

FETCH! ☐   Date taught................

EAT UP, BOY! ☐   Date taught..........?.....

HEEL! ☑   Date taught............?.....

2. Incredibly Useful Dog-Handling Commands

DAWN BOY! ☐   Date taught................

EAT UP THAT BOY! ☐   Date taught................

How To Handle Your Cat: Stage Six

Your Very Own Purr-sonal Cat File

YOUR CAT'S NAME

(i) WHEN IT'S BEHAVING ITSELF

.... *Miss Miss* ....

(ii) WHEN IT'S NOT BEHAVING ITSELF

.... *Menaces* ....

YOUR CAT'S CATTY-GORY (tick box)

Bird Cat	Chicken Cat	Spider Cat
☐	☐	☑

Owl Cat	Boa Constrictor Cat	Other (please specify)
☐	☐	.......*None*.....

PEOPLE YOUR CAT CAN HELP YOU HANDLE

Gran	Big Brother's Girlfriend	Little Sister
☐	☐	☐

Dad	Killer Sharkey	Any other (please specify)
☑	☐	.......*None*.....